To Dan and Joyce —

Always celebrate your,

friends !!

Hal Danzig
Dianne (Evans) Danzig

Shakespeare Lives On Cape Cod
(and everywhere else!)

BOB DANZIG

Shakespeare Lives On Cape Cod
(and everywhere else!)

BOB DANZIG

DISCO
MAMBO

DISCO MAMBO HEADQUARTERS: Menlo Park, CA

CURRENT PRINTING: 10 9 8 7 6 5 4 3 2 1
Cover and interior design by Sarah E. Barr, sarahebarr@gmail.com

Paintings by Dianne Evans

www.bobdanzig.com

ISBN-978-0-615-29930-3

Printed in Korea

Every book is a reflection of creative whispers
guiding the author. This work is a mirror
of those whispers from many.
It is enhanced by the original Cape Cod scenes
captured by the gifted local artist, Dianne Evans.
My gratitude is great for the abundance of her
shared gifts—and the whispers of so many.
You know who you are. As do I.
Thank you.

Contents

Invitations VIII

Foreword XI

1: Enter or Exit 2

2: Ramrod Straight 6

3: The Hand Off 12

4: A Slice of Orange 18

5: Sea Legs 22

6: Flashing Neon Signs 30

7: Porcelain Doll 34

8: Store-Front Windows 38

9: Clip Clip 44

10: Stem Support 50

11: A Best Friend 54

12: Lean On Me 58

13: Need to Need to Need 64

14: Doing it Our Way 72

15: The Race is On 78

16: Goobers or Licorice Sticks? 84

17: Rafael's Cupcake 92

18: One O'clock Walk to the Mailbox . . . 98

19: The Magnetic Personality 104

20: Butterfly Splendor 110

Reflections 113

 *Invitations*

There may be only a few who thumb these pages, whose lives are dulled with loneliness—with quiet desperation to find joy, meaning, illumination, even simple fresh friendships.

And for those few this message of the cocoon dancing pals may be just the candle of new light you are seeking to fill voids and purpose in your life.

The message is to move out, move on, move forward to put yourself into situations that engage you and other people. These need not be deep or complex programs, but they do require you to take that action step and embrace common interests with other people.

Look for local library reading groups, look for adult school study programs, look for area dance lesson groups, look for any interesting program that merely requires you to seek it out and join it.

Loneliness is a choice. Abundant living is also a choice. Should you be one of those gripped in low-level sadness—with no sense of greater purpose to your life—determine this minute to reach up, reach out and find new joy with new faces, new friends, new purpose.

And as one embraces common interests with others—functioning in your own shared activities—seek opportunities to build a cocoon of caring, of support, of "being there" for each other.

Those opportunities are the building blocks in creating those "cocoons of comfort."

Work to understand the reality of the spectrum of human conditions, issues, life journeys represented in each individual member of your cocoon.

Shakespeare's works endure because he captured basic truths of the human condition.

Every member of your shared activity deserves the respect and understanding for their own life issues. When in your cocoon of comfort—those life issues are made more manageable—less threatening.

It is when you can nurture a shared activity to become a caring, nurturing, supportive element that the notion of a cocoon can embrace your life.

# Foreword

"YES-YES-YES" was the collective chant as the dancers shared the songs of the popular band.

It was Friday night—tradition night, launch-the-weekend night.

As was their weekly tradition, the friends first gathered at the local yacht club's rectangular-shaped, nautical-themed, shining-wood bar, featuring a spectacular view of the ocean, through oversized windows.

I was invited to join them, and "observe" this group of friends who shared their lives on Cape Cod (their more permanent home) and in Florida (where they spent winters).

Their friendships are broad, inclusive, rich—beaming with celebration of life.

Ballroom dancing brought them together and then became the glue bonding their friendships. The glue was made more biting as they sought out dance spots featuring bands that played happy memories-invoking music. Those past memories were infused into their current dance, a delightful mix of past and present.

The sound of their bantering voices grew to a low rumble, punctuated by bursts of laughter, and enthusiastic phrasing that popped up and out of the rumble throughout the night. It was easy to tell that this was a gathering of pals.

The ease with which they spoke to each other, the level of comfort, and the patience and attention they showered upon each other confirmed the richness of their friendships.

Even without words, the bond was apparent. Handshakes, hugs, gentle pats on the back, "air kisses" and waves were constants throughout the night.

Some looked dressed to match the bar's nautical theme, while others were attired in loud florals. Then there were those that embraced the traditional Cape Cod "look" of casual slacks and sweaters draped over their shoulders, with the arms tied loosely in front, falling just above their chest. They were ready for the cool air from the ocean, which often arrived as the sunset departed.

From the loud to the conservative, their outer differences were welcomed in the group. Their common love of dancing was always up front. The backstage differences were indicators of each individual's personality—and were always welcomed. They embraced their differences in addition to their shared interests.

Though they start their evenings at a bar, alcohol is rarely a part of the evening—some drink ice tea, some sip coffee, and others glasses of water. A few have beers or wine. They aren't there for the drinks, but for the dancing, the conversations, the friendships.

I could see that they were in harmony with one another. I wondered how others might learn from this group of friends—how they might be encouraged to join a group of people and help nurture it into a deep pool of care for one another.

This started out as a dance group. In the beginning, no one envisioned it becoming such a strong support group of friends— informal yet absolute.

My mind's eye sees a cocoon when I think about them. Those within the cocoon are insulated, cared for, nurtured. At the same time, each person grows as an individual. This cocoon features numerous butterflies, all growing together, but all very different— all individuals.

As the evening hours pass, their talk turns to dinner. Where will they sup? Who will call ahead to arrange enough tables for them to all eat together? After years of asking the same questions, the answers easily follow. They discuss a few restaurants with great local bands—where they can dance and dine. When they leave the yacht club, a few do so with dance steps leading the way outside.

At dinner, the constant rumble of the bantering turns to a staccato— with conversation arriving in short bursts, between bites of dinner. The pitch is a little higher, indicating excitement and the dancing that will soon follow. As dinner comes to a close, pairs start to peel away to start dancing.

Though they don't dance in one large group, they seem to move as one—no sharp divisions, stress or gaping seams. They are still in their cocoon.

Each person who walked into the yacht club, who supped and delighted in the banter, and who moved his or her happy feet over the dance floor, ultimately returned home, without the group of friends, to engage and explore a new tomorrow, often emerging from the cocoon alone.

The benefit of the cocoon is that the nurturing prepares each butterfly to gradually leave the cocoon, slipping through the opening, spreading his or her wings, and flying. Though some of the butterflies struggle, there are others, who have shared the cocoon, who are there to help.

That cocoon offers them the support to navigate the Shakespearian dramas of their individual lives, when they are not dancing or dining with friends on Friday nights.

Those dramas—and sometimes comedies—reflect the perpetual elements of human nature that have caused Shakespeare's works to be relevant over so many generations. There are certain themes that transcend time, and which are relied upon, valued, and cherished in relationships around the world and through the years.

Contemplate those lasting themes that punctuate the rich works of the bard:

Wisdom	*Unity*	*Courage*
Family	*Loyalty*	*Hope*
Romance	*Joy*	*Love*
Kindness	*Trust*	*Truth*

These themes sustain the influence of Shakespeare. They are rooted in everlasting elements of the human condition.

The permanence of it all creates its' wonder.

Varying peoples of varying backgrounds, varying life patterns, and varying influences, sharing the unvaried elements of the soul, the heart—the inexplicable impulses of the human nature—is what stimulates the ongoing welcoming of Shakespeare's works.

Whenever groups of people congregate—as different as they may be in coming to the groups—their lives mirror varying degrees of these themes. As with the characters in many of Shakespeare's plays, individuals today must navigate the inevitable ups and downs that appear when the various themes merge.

This is a commentary on what creates such a group on Cape Cod–and everywhere else.

Thus, *Shakespeare Lives On Cape Cod–And Everywhere Else!*

Shakespeare Lives On Cape Cod–And Everywhere Else! was inspired by the group of dancing friends. It is a series of stories rooted in the lives of various people I have known through the years. No one story represents the real life of any one individual. Rather, these stories represent common threads featured in Shakespeare's work, which are also shared by so many people, living similar stories–time, place, and names are the differences.

The Cape Cod paintings punctuating the book flow from the gifted imagination and artistic hands of Dianne Evans. They are the backdrop to this set of stories, and to so many others.

1- Enter or Exit

Pam and Renee are pals—true pals, alike in so many ways: Both are former teachers and young widows. Both are stylish, with glittering personalities. Both love to dance. Both treasure being in the cocoon of Cape Cod friends.

They are like twins, but with a whiff of difference.

Pam learned she had lymphnode cancer on the same day that Renee learned that her mood swings reflected a chemical imbalance in her brain. Both were advised their conditions were treatable, manageable: medications for Renee and radiation for Pam.

Pam chose to embrace her challenge and vigorously pursue her path to wellness. Renee lapsed into a dark downward spiral. She did not want to depend on prescription drugs.

Both stopped dancing.

While receiving radiation, Pam lacked the energy to dance. At the same time, Renee withdrew from her cocoon pals. She became distant, inaccessible, and largely alone as the devil of mood swings became thunder storms drowning her optimism and joy.

Though she lacked the energy to dance, Pam did not put her life on hold. Her marriage had been a happy one. She didn't want to replace her husband, but she did want to meet someone who brought her the same joy. The radiation treatments forced her to try something new. She explored meeting people online. Though all she met were interesting, Chuck was compelling. Pam shared her health challenges with Chuck as they became closer. He told her he wanted to be her partner in that battle.

During one visit to Renee's darkened home, Pam showed Renee the web site, on which she was introduced to Chuck.

"All I had to do was hit the ENTER button", she said. "You can do the same. Just try it."

Renee looked at Pam and responded: "The only key I want to press is the EXIT key."

Pam's love for Renee prevented Renee from acting on that choice. She visited Renee twice a week until Renee chose the key to a better tomorrow.

Encouraged by Pam's persistence, Renee finally agreed to start taking the doctor-prescribed medical treatment. Her dark moods abated.

During a visit with Pam, Renee submitted a description of herself on the dating site that Pam used. Though Renee's own marriage had been strained, Pam's friendship encouraged Renee to try something new. That decision—to hit the ENTER button—made it possible for her to meet Carl.

Pam and Chuck are now married. Though Pam's health challenge is not yet behind her, her every day life brings the beauty of a caring partner to make each day shine.

Carl is a treasured part of Renee's life. When Renee chose to hit the ENTER button on her computer, she accessed a lovely new screen of life.

2 - *Ramrod Straight*

Punctuating the pebble-stoned gardens surrounding the Rodin Sculpture Garden, at Stanford University's Cantor Arts Center in Palo Alto, California, are the multiple statues crafted by the great sculptor, Rodin.

Each is black. Each is a perpetual presence depicting the emotional range of mankind—as it is expressed physically in statue form.

The statues do not move. They do not yield to the changes of seasons. They simply ARE.

Yet, their absoluteness, their muscular tone, their embrace of everyman's life paths causes them to be mystical, inviting, mesmerizing. They cannot expect to be more than the statues which they are.

Memories of those interestingly contemplative Rodin statues are stimulated upon seeing the regular presence of Bill perched at his end-seat barstool. He sits as if standing: shoulders squared, neck firm, still-muscular body rippling through his always-black shirt.

Bill sits ramrod straight, stone-faced. His neat white hair is combed to precision. His leathered face is statue-like—handsomely Romanesque—yet statue-like in a mask of sameness. Absent expression.

The dancers in his cocoon of friends sense Bill's hardening, his adoption of a statue-like presence. He is camouflaging the pain of criticizing-away his dance partner, Louise.

Bill and Louise were fluid on the dance floor, but their talk didn't match their walk—or in this case, their dancing.

Louise cautioned Bill to curb his tendency to criticize—to find fault—to amplify tiny flaws.

Her warnings elevated to mandate that Bill stop—just stop—causing her so much discomfort with his habit of criticism.

Warnings slid off Bill. Mandates were ignored.

Louise gathered up the courage to finally tell Bill she would no longer be his regular dance partner. She would only agree to a more distant friendship—even an occasional dance—but would no longer endure another assault of criticism.

Now Bill rarely criticizes another who is close to him—because no one is close to him.

Bill sips his drink slowly, steadily. Staring into the amber fluid he SEES his habit of life-long criticism as if it were tangible, real.

He sees Louise in the darkness of the drink beckoning to him to shed the old—embrace the new. His heart jumps at the pull of dancing openly, completely absent that habit of criticism.

His great wish is to BE among the free flowing, happy dancers.

However, he knows it is work in progress. Bill is not yet there.

Thus, he is perched—ramrod straight—on that bar stool. He is Cape Cod's own Rodin statue— seeking the elusive warmth of joy.

Then one evening—slowly— shoulders slumped as he struggles, conviction sets in that he will make a determined effort to curb that habit of criticism. His plan? Bite his tongue whenever that nasty habit peeks out.

It took a sore mouth before he felt he was conquering the habit. Not yet perfect—but clearly progressing—as his sore tongue testified.

Progress sufficient for him to call Louise and ask her to join him for dinner. She agreed to see Bill one more time.

After being seated at the candlelit table, Louise asked: "What's new?"

"I have a mouth full of canker sores—self inflicted—but my criticism habit has been converted to compliments," Bill replied. He then told her of his almost silly—but effective—commitment to bite his tongue whenever the criticism genie tried to get out of the bottle.

"By the by," he said, "You look lovely. It is my great privilege to be with you tonight."

The statue had finally become fluid and malleable. It was a new day for Bill.

Ramrod Straight - 10

3 - The Hand Off

Every graduate wore the same cap and gown—gold tassel hanging off the right side—occasionally brushing a cheek as the slight wind of graduation day nudged the tassels.

Kathy noticed the sea of caps and gowns around her. It felt good to be a part of this group. These weren't her dancing pals. These were the young twenty-something-year-old graduates that her pals had encouraged her to join years earlier. She wore the same cap and gown, but she was different.

Just out of high school, Kathy chose to be married, rather than to be a college student. She was the only member of her family to make that decision.

It was not a healthy choice. She was young and hadn't found her "voice." Her spouse criticized more than he praised. She felt "lesser" for too long. When she finally decided to move on, she found herself moving right back into the same relationship. She'd found the courage to leave one husband, but didn't find the courage to stand on her own two feet.

Not wanting to tell her family of another "failed" marriage, she pretended to glide, as she stumbled through one attempt after another to achieve her much-wanted "happily ever after." While she devoted herself to making that second marriage work, it seemed the devotion was a one-way street. In fact, she decided, a dead end. She ended it.

Then she started dancing, found friends who encouraged her, who invested in her, who were devoted to her.

And then she stopped drifting.

And then she started anew.

She became a college student.

She loved saying those words when she was asked: "What are you doing these days?"

Her enthusiastic answer: "I am attending college."

She worked a full-time job while she was a full-time student.

Her days were calibrated carefully so she could squeeze in her job, homework, classes and all those everyday chores of a life being lived.

There were high-stress moments when Kathy looked in the mirror and asked herself: How can I do all this? Why am I doing all this?

She reminded herself that after years of working so hard, for so long, to make others happy, she was finally investing in herself, just as her dancing pals had invested in her.

She learned to stand on her own two feet—and to jump high, twist, turn, double-step. She was able to smile when she struggled, because the struggle was without pain this time. Trying to "do it all" was hard, but it was all about her this time around.

And then came a brilliantly sunny day with only a slight breeze nudging her graduation cap, as her proud family and dancing cocoon friends gathered to celebrate her—at her college graduation commencement.

In a line with the hundreds of graduates—less than half her age—Kathy heard her name called and again put her foot forward. Step by step she put one foot in front of the other, almost gliding (no stumbling this time) toward the college's president. He said her name aloud—clear and sharp—suggesting his own personal pride in seeing this adult woman choose to BE a college graduate.

He smiled as he held out her leather-bound diploma as it moved from his hand to Kathy's hand.

Hand Off.

Her fingers touched the extended fingers of the president. She felt an electric jolt.

An affirmation of her college—conquered.

A cheer arose from Kathy's gathered fans.

They knew—as she would know—this was not just another graduation. It was a celebration of her endurance, her determination, her sacrifices—and her forward step approach to life.

She had chosen TO BE.

Now retired from her post-college professional work in the Social Services field, Kathy is on Cape Cod, surrounded by her dancing, caring, loving pals.

She is comfortable in a relationship, but quick to advise marriage of no interest: "Out of my system," she says.

Watching her radiant smile as she dances, one notes she seems to favor the steps that invite her to go forward—TO BE. Observers note that Kathy's tone and spirit lift—heighten—when she describes that magical moment of "The Hand-Off."

4 - A Slice of Orange

No order needed.

The moment a cocoon member enters the restaurant and dance club, The Harbor Inn, the always-smiling host and bartender, Charlie, promptly has that patron's favored drink on the table—fresh and waiting.

Charlie knows, for example, that Dianne favors a sparkling water with a large slice of orange nestled on the glass rim. He glances occasionally as the water level moves down to an inch or so—the orange slice gripped in Dianne's two fingers, and nibbled down to the rind. Experience taught Charlie that when the rind is no longer afloat it is re-fill time.

Charlie also knows the bands that attract most of the cocoon dancers, making them "regulars." He has long-cultivated a sense of which bands are dance pleasers.

Inexplicably, without notice, Charlie learned that a new owner had decided to change the band to one that appealed to a younger audience.

The owner did not consider the risk of chasing off the regulars, most adult cocoon dancers. He also failed to consider that a young audience would not buy dinners.

With no compatible music, the cocoon crowd drifted off to another local club which, while the music was friendly, did not have a large dance floor—or Charlie. The hosts at the new club did not know Dianne's favorite drink. They didn't know how much she favored those slices of oranges.

In time, The Harbor Inn's owner realized his mistake. Now desperate to regain the cocoon crowd, he turned to Charlie to rebuild the club prospects.

Now having to rely on once-informal contacts to help re-build, Charlie first considered the very best, most danceable bands he could engage. He took the risk of actually hiring them for Friday and Saturday nights before he began his campaign to bring back the cocoon dancers.

After a few weeks of calling folks, one by one, and describing the music being offered, the earlier clients began to slowly return to The Harbor Inn to dance.

When Dianne walked in for the first return evening, Charlie, bursting in welcome smile, quickly poured the sparkling water, with sliced orange, and had it at Dianne's table before she sat down.

Charlie had taken action—invited fresh unity—had found the musical key to reconciliation.

He recognized that sometimes people like knowing how much you favor the slice of orange.

"Frailty, thy name is woman."

5 - Sea Legs

It was rare. Unique. Unprecedented. Unexpected. Margot announced to her family she had decided to join the U.S. Navy.

Just out of college, with a full career ahead of her as a Biology teacher, she watched her family struggle with the implications of her leaning toward naval service.

She explained the pull of service to the nation that had given her so much opportunity—including her full scholarship to college—and the notion of sailing a naval ship to distant ports.

In her private moments she also whispered to herself that she was tired, just tired of the dating scene in her area. Most of the men she knew were rough—centered on bowling or hunting or fishing. She had yet to meet anyone who seemed centered on Margot.

She was described by all as sophisticated, educated, an easy elegance to her manner—and always as neat as one could be. The idea of a complete change of scenery—with a new cast—made her feet dance.

Following enlistment, the Navy trained her to be an accomplished sonar specialist. Her finely-tuned eyesight, combined with her aptitude for discerning even distant light signals, made her a dependable asset on the ship.

Margot was sea worthy—a natural sailor—at home on the ship, within a few miles of the home harbor.

It was on her first long-distance ocean trip that she found herself challenged by the ship tossing in the more violent storm waves pummeling the ship and rocking violently. She developed a balance problem.

Margot was out of commission when gripped by the balance issue. It only eased when she lay on her canvas strip of a bunk in the very bowels of the ship. The female sailor quarters—separated from the men—mirrored the men's area: tight blanket folded like skin on the bunk, small pillow tucked in the lip of the blanket like a newborn kangaroo.

A half-sized locker with three shelves embraced those few personal items that reminded the locker user that they WERE individual human beings, as well as cogs in the delicate machine of sailor competencies that brought function to the ship. Each mattered as an individual. Each mattered as a central player in the ship's mission.

As the early signs of "imbalance" shrieked at Margot, she would scurry to the relative calm of that tidy bunk. Her superior officers and fellow crew members expressed understanding and sympathy for her "sea leg" challenge.

Despite that empathy, Margot felt incomplete, an addendum to the ongoing story of her shipmates as they conquered the angry ocean, while she lay struggling with her imbalance.

She dreamt about being a 'complete' sailor—not an occasional one. She wanted to be steady. She wanted to be balanced.

One of her shipmates, Gil, had met Margot during two separate ship exercises. He was instantly struck by her lady-like femininity. He was "wowed" by her competency as a sonar expert. He wondered about those times when she was simply gone. Not there. Disappeared.

Gil was shy. He was tentative about having the courage to speak to Margot outside the general ship exercises. Yet, he was drawn to her and wanted to work toward a shipmate friendship.

Despite his hesitancy, he asked one of Margot's pals, Lydia, about her absence. Lydia explained Margot's balance issue, which pinned her down, lying flat, on her own bunk whenever the ship confronted choppy seas.

As the ocean turbulence quieted and Margot returned to her duties, Gil was bursting with delight to see her. He leapt past his shyness and rushed to her side during the lunch in the ship mess hall.

Pink faced in his shyness, he blurted out that he missed seeing her happy face and was pleased she was back on her feet.

Margot had never noticed Gil. She was busy at her sonar duties—was consumed with doing more—always more—when the calmer sea permitted her to compensate for work duties missed when not balanced. She was consumed with the notion she was not doing her part all the time.

For the first time, as she listened to Gil's concern, she noticed him.

He was tall, ruddy cheeked, longish face, coal-black hair—handsome in his strong presence.

She found his interest sweet.

She also found his interest a stark contrast to the young men in her pre-Navy orbit.

What she had not told her parents and friends about her decision to enlist in the Navy was that she found the young men around her boorish, crude, and rough hewn, like sandpaper.

Margot decided that her universe needed widening if she were ever to find comfort, a caring way, genuine love from—and for—a life partner.

As Gil found more ways to be with Margot—attending ship movies together, playing cribbage with other small clusters of sailor-players—he and she found two combined phenomenon:

- His shyness dipped until gone altogether when he was with her.
- Her balance problems slowly abated as her mind and heart became more accepting of Gil.

It happened that their Navy enlistment terms were up at the same time—within a few months of each other.

Before leaving the ship, Gil proposed to Margot and told her they would live wherever she chose to live.

Margot completed her Navy service and chose Cape Cod as the place she wanted to pot her life.

In time they settled into a new life partnership and, loving to dance, became welcome dancer pals in the cocoon of friends.

Whenever new folks meet them for the first time, they inevitably observe how secure and confident Gil is. Shyness is a memory. They also point to Margot's steadiness—her very balanced way.

Gil and Margot bring steady sea legs to their new ship of life on Cape Cod.

The occasional choppy seas of life washed by them. They brought the shine of consistency to their own life chapter and spread that shine among their cocoon pals.

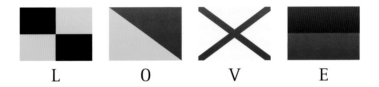

L   O   V   E

6 - *Flashing Neon Signs*

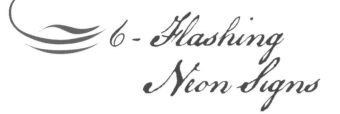

Once punctuating the roadsides of America, flashing neon signs would invite traveling families to speak their familiar messages aloud when driving by them. Indeed, a repeat trip over familiar roads—with those now-familiar slogans flashing away—would prompt the families to sing their glistening messages. It was their familiarity, their dependable sameness, their touches of wit that invited the comfort of simply seeing them, passing them, reading them.

Randy and Mitch are like those signs, just without the flashing neon colors. When their cocoon friends gather for their weekend dance get-togethers, they know the first table next to the band, facing the dance floor, will host the two buddies, Randy and Mitch, seated side by side.

The dance club attracts a steady stream of mature, often single, dancers. The dependable presence of Randy and Mitch promises

a partner for any dance offered by the band. They are both good rhythm dancers. No one has to sit on the sidelines.

As a pair they are dependable. Friends expect to see them there and enjoy them. They look like opposites, but the differences are only on the surface. Randy has a full crop of curly grey hair and is still high-school-graduation lean. Mitch is compactly robust, with his hair and beard shaped and straight. They share being "dependable buddies" at that table. They share quick smiles and good humor, and they share being smooth step dancers.

Never a need to plan their weekends. They would simply be there, smiling, ready to dance.

They have a "get to know me" aura about them. When cocoon pals arrive at the club, they see those two familiar faces and are invited to feel the familiar warmth shared with the driving families welcomed by those familiar flashing neon signs.

It is easy to let one's imagination float to seeing signs flashing at the table of Randy and Mitch, flashing the words:

"WELCOME"
"ENJOY" **"RELAX"**
"TAP A TOE"
"PICK YOUR DANCE"
"WE ARE HERE"
"RANDY & MITCH"
"DANCING BUDDIES"

Inherent in their presence is a tinge of melancholy for the life chapter that preceded the "buddies" sharing that table: partners passing away; careers ending; life chapters ticking away and shortening.

But the melancholy disappears quickly as they stand, bow, move a partner to the dance floor. Their implied flashing sign reads:

"BUDDIES, SIMPLY BUDDIES."

7 - Porcelain Doll

The shine to her was luminous—emitting a light beam of invitation, to come close to her doll-like loveliness. Her dancing cocoon pals teased her for having a face that could be a model for doll makers. She, they observed, looked perfectly porcelain.

Because Theresa had heard those most genuine compliments all her life, she determined—at a very early age—to insure her life was about abundance that went beyond her porcelain beauty.

When she was younger, she volunteered as a hospital candy striper, cheerfully visiting patients, chatting amiably while offering an array of magazines and books for the patients to consider.

Of course, most patients quickly remarked on her truly beautiful face. Theresa learned to accept those compliments with grace and always turned the conversation back to the patients and their lives. She learned as a teen the key comfort tool of caring about the other person made for more successful conversations.

That lesson stayed with Theresa as the years unfolded—past college, past career, past marriage, past family. Theresa was a practiced talent who could amplify a symphony of personal relations by simply caring about the comfort of the other person with her.

Life's stumbles and moments of despair were as true and certain in Theresa's life as in all people. Her resiliency to better deal with these was anchored in the fact her porcelain doll-like loveliness invited warmth from others. That 'bounce back' quality was also anchored in her consistent choice to be a giver, a caring person who focused on others.

Over time, Theresa's porcelain doll-like features retreated subtly so people noticed the luster of her character, her giving manner, her effervescent cheerfulness first.

What few knew was that Theresa had kept a collection of dolls throughout her life. They were almost companions in her mind.

In private moments—as she struggled to incent people to go past her porcelain beauty—she would talk aloud to those dolls. In her mind's eye she would hear their guiding answers when she asked how to behave in order to cause people to see her full person—not just her doll-like features.

Of course, only silence greeted her as her dolls perched silently, there to listen, but not to answer. In time, as she created her own pathways to serve others, she came to view the silence as a beacon light of instruction. The words of instruction she heard, flowing from those dolls, in her mind's eye were:

Be As You Be

Choose What You Wish To Be

Treasure Both

These instructional words became her mantra. Theresa came to accept her porcelain, shining beauty—as she came to commit herself to a lifetime of being a willing servant to others.

By the time she retired and happily located on Cape Cod, she had come to that daily commitment to accept what "she be"—to nurture and treasure her choice to "Be what she wished to be."

When a new friend invited her to dance at a local club, she quickly embraced new friends and became one of the cocoon dancing pals. While everyone admires her still porcelain, doll-like features, they deeply loved her for her consistent demonstration of her choice to be a caring, loving, friend to each of them.

Theresa's shining porcelain is as deeply impressive for what she is inside—as it is for how she looks outside.

8 - Store-Front Windows

Not unlike children clustered for warmth, pressing against each other, as they squished noses against the store-front windows during the holidays, Louis was always separated from the desirables by a window-like shield.

Those exuberant children could look—but not touch—and surely could not have those abundant treats. Within eyesight, but not to be held.

Louis is twice divorced. He is a caring, responsible father, but success as a husband avoided him.

Now in his mid sixties, he remains light of foot and is a willing dance partner for fellow cocoon pals. His skin is still smooth, relatively unlined. He has a pleasant face, with rose-tinged cupid lips, framed by tidy, sandy hair. He favors floral-designed shirts hanging loose over his barrel chest and belt.

The holiday store-front windows of his childhood embraced a holiday magic with two window displays. One had a tiny train on a track, wending in a large oval that hugged the entire perimeter of the display. The other was a roller coaster, the frames of which were snow covered in white glitter. Moving up the roller coaster were holiday carved swing seats—green and red—with doll-like figurine couples in various poses of intimacy. Some hugged, some kissed, and some smiled into their partners' eyes. All with legs covered by miniature fur-like blankets.

Even as an adult, Louis is transfixed by the figurines, wondering to himself why he was not able to join them on the other side of the window, for a hug, kiss, and embrace.

With his cocoon pals, he felt destined to dance with, but only view, their hugs, kisses, and embraces through the cool glass of a slim window barricading him from that fullness of intimacy. He was allowed on the outside portion of the window. He was dependable, steady, a good dancer, but nothing more.

Given that reality, Louis learned to accept comfort in being accepted only as a companion for occasional meals and outings. After such moments of friendship, Louis would recall walking past a neighborhood bakery as a boy, when the fragrance of fresh baked bread drifted from the open door. He would stop and breathe that aroma deep enough to actually taste the bread. He became satisfied, as if he'd taken an actual bite of the bread himself.

Though Louis could not bite the real bread, just as he could not be in the holiday window, he coaxed himself into enjoying the implication of the bread, and feeling the joy of watching the holiday window train puffing along to cross under the roller coaster with the doll figures in perpetual intimacy.

Then came the night when Louis dreamt he was pressed against the holiday window, watching the display designer adjusting the display. She had seen Louis during his many visits to that magical window. She waved Louis into the store where she greeted him and invited him to actually join her inside the window display itself.

Guided by her instructions, Louis moved the glittering roller coaster a few inches to correct its position. He gingerly touched the tiny figurines in their perpetual hugs, kisses, and embraces, finally joining those couples. But something was missing. After wishing to be a part of this display for such a long time, he realized that it was not real. The couples were merely cast-iron figurines.

He awoke from the dream, blinked his eyes for a moment, and saw the reality of his having been accepted fully into the holiday window of all his dancing cocoon pals. In his mind's eye he saw himself whirling around the dance floor, arm embracing a dance mate, knowing that he was a part of the magic of the display. He also knew that he could enjoy the magic inside, while living on the outside. He had chosen to live from the outside, never thinking the magic inside would be shared with him.

Louis thought about the lesson of accepting the joy of what one has. He accepted the comfort of that reality with no sense of limitation going forward.

"What's in a name?
That which we
call a Rose."

9 - Clip Clip

Sturdy shoes, a winning smile, a tender touch, and talent with the scissors, helped Harvey grow a devoted list of regulars at his barber shop.

Every head of hair differed, as did the personality and bantering chat of every client. For all, Harvey worked to the soothing beat of the clipping scissors and the buzzing electric trimmers.

During the down-time between clients, Harvey often rested his eyes while exercising his mind. He liked to count, and created a game he called "Duration." He'd play this game at least once a week, thinking about the average hours he'd worked that week—about 48—multiplied by his 50 plus years as a barber. His personal duration led him to over 125,000 hours and growing. He'd also think about the different people he'd met during those years, and the ones who became a part of his life.

He was a young barber, with five years under his belt when he met his Janey. On their 50th wedding anniversary, as they danced together in front of their family and friends, they celebrated 50 years of love. They were partners on and off the dance floor—whether they were learning new dance steps, or encouraging their three children to take their first steps.

The growth of their marriage was much like that of Harvey's rose garden. Harvey and Janey were supports for each other's growth. They cultivated their relationship, cherishing the blooms of each Spring. When they weren't growing, they'd concentrate on what they could do to ensure the greatest amount of joy and beauty in the garden of roses and in their marriage. One year—completely by accident—Harvey made a discovery.

When he first opened his barber shop, he often mused about what else could be done with the hair he swept up each day. There were bags of it left over by the time the final regular said goodbye and Harvey clicked the lock on the door and headed home in the evening.

He suggested Janey create small knitted dolls—she loved to knit—and stuff them with the soft clipped hair. She tried doing this with a few dolls, but the hair made a mess and caused her to sneeze.

He thought about a more useful approach. He mixed the hair in with the birdseed he used to fill his feeders. The birds could pick through the hair to find the seeds. The squirrels, he hoped, would have a harder time, and finally leave the feeders alone, for good.

Harvey was disappointed when he saw the squirrels picking the hair out and tossing it to the ground. That's when he discovered a secret, and when he became thankful for having such crafty squirrels in his yard.

The roses beneath the feeder began to blossom with a vigor, a crisp beauty, and a rich fragrance that made them stand-outs among the other roses in the yard. It was a "voila" moment for Harvey. The hair tossed aside by the birds and squirrels was fertilizing the roses.

Harvey continued bringing home bags of clipped hair, and then spreading it near the roots of the roses throughout his garden. The roses reached heights, colors, fragrances, unachieved in the past.

They also invited neighbor admiration. In time, the roses became a landmark of pride for locals who knew Harvey had a "secret" garden.

While he did not directly share his secret, he enjoyed the game of hinting, particularly to the dancing pals in his cocoon of dancing friends. When they asked about his roses, he would say: "Janey is the rose of my life. She's my precious flower. She is the secret." They never guessed that he was referring to Janey's hair. Sometimes he would add: "You, my friend, are the secret to all things beautiful in my life." Those friends who were also regulars at Harvey's barber shop had no idea how their hair cuts propelled the growth of the garden.

In time, after all those years of hearing the "clip clip" of his scissors, Harvey sold his shop, and reduced his work hours to a day and a half a week at another shop. His long-time customers are pleased he is still available for them. They still enjoy asking about the hours in his "Duration" game, and probing for his rose garden secret. He always smiles at the latter, replying: "Janey's hair is beautiful, but it is her heart that I truly love."

He still packs up the bag of clippings, mixing them with his Janey's cut hair, and sprinkles them throughout the treasured garden. The roses burst forth with magnificent loveliness, just as his Janey burst forth with her loveliness to make Harvey's life such a treasured garden.

10 - Stem Support

The polish on the shining new hardwood floors reflected the sunlight drifting through the windows in Bonnie's kitchen. In fact, every floor in the new lake-view home built for her by, son, Larry, had that same brand-new shine.

Bonnie had moved her antique, wooden kitchen table, and living room and bedroom sets from her city apartment to this new home— one of six being constructed by her builder son.

Doll house tidy, neat, cozy, and easy to navigate, Bonnie's new home only required the normal adjustment to the "different" as well as the insight that her children wished for her to be "in view" as they monitored her new and complex health issues.

That lake view, while peaceful from her front-porch vantage point, was just that—a lake view. No neighborhood, no familiar easy-to-reach stores, no church to walk to, and no cocoon dancing pals at the easy beckoning. It was an adjustment and recognition that years sliding by had contained within them the reality that, like most people, Bonnie was, sliding by. Her enforced recent focus on myriad health issues had, understandably, slowed her pace—limited her energy to dance as freely as she had in the past.

Bonnie was flower-like. A strong stem provided her the strength to be the caregiver to her long-ill spouse and then to be a potent single parent, guiding her three children. When her husband died, Bonnie stepped back. Like a flower in the Fall, her blooms were worn, tired, and ready to sleep. However, Bonnie had the strength of that stem, which didn't want to fade, which wanted to grow on, wide awake and blooming through Fall and Winter, and into each new following season.

In the Fall of her life, she started dancing. She had been a strong flower, living alone, taking care of her family, outside the garden. When she started dancing, she joined a garden. She became an important part of the landscape. Within that cocoon, she met Bruno, dated him, and grew to love him. In her chapter of health challenges, Bruno showed the same strong stem, able to support and help Bonnie as she had helped her own husband in the past.

Though she'd always been the northern version of a Steel Magnolia—and her will is still strong—her body is featherlike. In her mind's eye, she moves in the breeze, like the long-branches of a willow, rustling softly in the wind.

As the cocoon pals discussed Bonnie's new life situation—a bit more removed geographically and a bit more challenged physically—they framed an action plan to keep her tight within their cocoon. They set a calendar commitment defining which pals would visit Bonnie as singles, doubles, and small groups. They also defined who would be Bonnie's personal escort for shopping, beauty salon, and errands that fell between visits.

They committed to being the strong stems, supporting Bonnie. They surround her, invite her warm smile and personality, and go the distance to keep her within their cocoon. They are her champions, and her strong will cheers them on, basking in the love and friendship.

The cocoon undulates with dancing, caring, loving, and supporting—a strong stem infused into the cocoon.

11 - A Best Friend

Emily is tall, confident, handsome, elegant, and a take-charge-of-the-floor dancer with her cocoon pals. Her dress is tailored, smart, always with at least one flower-like color announcing her strong personality.

She is a former teacher, whose students adored her. Upon retirement she sought out Cape Cod as the place of happy childhood memories. She left the subtle scar tissue of a disappointing marriage—and another long and ultimately empty later relationship behind her. In her new Cape Cod life, she seeks the highs of life, not wanting to be swept into the low grey memories of yesterday. Despite her appetite for fun, her capacity for relaxation, and her enjoyment of the freedom and independence, soon after moving to Cape Cod she found herself yearning for something else from her childhood—her blankee.

Blankee is Emily's earliest childhood memory. The creamy white rectangle was covered in rosebuds on one side with pink and white

stripes on the other. The words "Emily's Blanket" were embroidered in pink at one corner. Blankee went everywhere with her—her constant companion. She spent hours holding the corner rubbing the edge against her cheek. She laughed, cried, and spoke her secret thoughts into Blankee.

Emily even brought Blankee to college with her. Her roommates' teasing prompted her to leave Blankee in the chest in her closet, after one long weekend visiting her parents. Through a disappointing marriage, Blankee stayed put.

Once on Cape Cod, though, Emily opened the old chest, and brought out her decades-old friend—tattered, edges frayed, color faded, and well loved.

Blankee reminds her that she needs a friend to listen, hear, and react without judgment. She needs reassurance when facing new situations, a sounding board before making decisions, the promise of a safe place—a comfort zone.

She knows that her cocoon friends live in the spirit of Blankee. They are her treasures. They support her, withholding all judgments. She laughs, cries, and shares her every day with them.

12 - Lean on Me

The band changed its pace and started up its next set with a polka. The lively music was met with applause and a few cheers as dancers quickly paired on the dance floor. The dancers stepped and hopped their way through the song. Those sitting, taking a break, smiled and tapped their toes, while bopping their heads to the beat. All eyes were glued to Roy, a stand-out among the other dancers.

Roy is one of the few cocoon pals who still dances the polka. At first glance, many guess him to be in his late sixties, perhaps early seventies. He is tall, lean, muscular—an easy stand-in for the famously fit, health guru Jack LaLanne. The knees and hips of many of his cocoon pals are too sensitive and weak to handle the hopping of the polka. Roy is the exception. At ninety years old, he can out-polka even the youngest dancers on the floor.

Roy takes pleasure in knowing he still has "it." He often engages in the carnival game of guessing other dancers' ages and asking them to guess his in return. The loser treats the winner to a round of drinks at the bar. Roy is always the winner. The other dancers see Roy's cocoon pals. They guess that he is older, but not ninety. Roy adds to the fun by offering the loser an opportunity to arm wrestle him—a chance to break even—but no one has taken him up on this offer. They want to have drinks with him. They enjoy sharing his love of life and of dance. It is when they see him with Lily that they see his gentler side.

After the polka, the band might play one more upbeat song, and then the music slows down again, offering everyone an opportunity to dance. This is when Roy wishes his friends at the bar a good evening, and gently leads the love of his life, Lily, to the floor.

Roy knows nature and good genes have treated him kindly. The same isn't true for his Lily. Where Roy can dance every dance, Lily can only dance a few, instead watching her Roy on the dance floor, delighting in how he leaves the others huffing and puffing in his wake. Roy has enough energy for both of them. He also has a caring nature, always in tune to Lily's needs and to the needs of their friends.

Lily loves to foxtrot, so Roy makes sure she has a few opportunities every time they meet with their dancing pals. Roy often approaches members of the band, and requests a fox trot. He signals to Lily from across the floor, waves to her, while pointing her out to the band. Though her body is frail and tree-limb thin, her smile is strong, and lights up the room. "Wouldn't you love to see her smile through an entire dance?" Roy always asks the band. "Just give me a song or two to go back to my love, and walk her to the floor," he adds. The band always agrees.

Walking to the dance floor, Roy and Lily resemble a pairing of the Yin and Yang symbols. Their outward, physical shape and appearance is so opposite. He is Paul Bunyan to her frail form

Yet when they start dancing, the opposites melt away and they are one.

Roy encourages Lily throughout their dances, embracing her as she leans against him, gliding her effortlessly across the floor. Watching them took my breath away. Theirs is a quiet beauty. All other dancers fade into the background. And though you can hear the music, the soft words that Roy whispers to Lily are what you hear loudest: "Lean on me, my love." Lily's reply: "Leaning on you is when I'm happiest."

Though their birthdays celebrate advancing years, the cocoon friends know no age barriers. Romance, trust, love, friendship, the sharing of strengths, and the always open shoulders to lean on are their focuses

13 - Need to Need to Need

No one expected Maggie to become the CEO—the one who would guide the tiny local family insurance business to be a multi-million dollar regional powerhouse. As a child, she was a wisp of a girl, small in frame, petite. She was shy, kept to herself, and had the look of someone in need of help—in need of someone to take care of her.

Gradually she gained confidence, and then one day, when there was no one else in the family to take over, she took over. She nurtured the family business out of love for her family, and because that was her role to play. She would take care of the business. Being shy wasn't an option for Maggie. It was a hurdle that she no longer had the time or energy to jump, so she eliminated it.

Maggie's sister, Bea, was shy as well. She was more comfortable with books than with people, and pursued a career as a librarian.

Though she still needed to interact with people, it was always about her passion—books. Through those conversations, she, too, grew more confident speaking with others.

As the family business grew, Maggie invited Bea to be her companion at the many social gatherings that she was invited to attend. Maggie taught Bea how to dress for these events, and encouraged her to speak with other guests, and enjoy herself. Maggie always made certain that Bea knew she needed her—as a sister and as a friend.

Then everything changed. Maggie had always taken care of Bea, but within a few seconds, their worlds flipped upside down.

The ground was slick with rain from the night before. The grass and the driveway in the front of their home, and the cobblestone path and steps leading up to their front door, were covered in a thin layer of water.

Maggie walked out the front door, ready for another day at work. She stepped out onto the steps, just as she had so many times before, and slipped. As she fell in shock, her head hit the first step, and then banged against each following step. Just past the fifth step at the bottom, everything stopped. Her head bloody and her body motionless, Maggie lay in front of their house, crumbled.

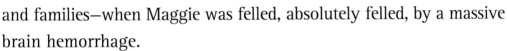

Bea rushed to her side, and put Maggie's head in her lap. Nothing. No Response. Bea screamed for help, ran inside and called 911, and then returned to Maggie, still on the ground, just as she'd been left.

It was a terrible, defining moment— etched in the memories of their friends and families—when Maggie was felled, absolutely felled, by a massive brain hemorrhage.

Bea rode in the ambulance to the hospital and accompanied Maggie on the transfer to a major head trauma facility. For several months after the accident, Bea was constantly at Maggie's side, always helping with the therapy effort.

When Maggie was able to move from complete dormancy to using a wheelchair, Bea was at her side, and brought her home. As Bea wheeled Maggie into the house, she knew their roles had changed. She would take care of Maggie, just as Maggie had taken care of her—at least that's what she hoped for in the beginning.

As weeks turned into months, Bea recognized that she needed help. Around the clock care for Maggie had taken its toll on Bea. She loved her sister and friend, but she, herself, was struggling to make it through each day. Enter Brenda.

Bea hired Brenda, a nurse, to help care for Maggie. In the end, Brenda's help also eased Bea's life. Bea now had some free time. For the first time in her life, instead of hiding in the library, she started visiting a nearby restaurant. The restaurant featured a live band and dance floor. After a few times dining there, Bea began to notice the regulars. She sat alone, watching the same group of friends dining, laughing, and dancing together. Her librarian tendency to shrink from public contact was too deeply embedded in her. She wanted to meet them, but remained an observer, separate and alone.

Over the next two years, Maggie gradually faded. Her eyes stopped lighting up when Bea smiled at her. Her appetite waned, and her already-petite body grew frail.

Bea and Brenda became friends, working together to make Maggie comfortable. Brenda also provided Bea with sister-like comfort, always kind, listening to Bea as she spoke about Maggie and the end they both knew was coming.

The morning finally arrived when Maggie didn't open her eyes. She'd passed away during the night.

Brenda helped Bea with the funeral arrangements, and as relatives and friends visited the home, it was Brenda who met them at the door and brought them in to where Bea sat, mourning Maggie's passing.

After Maggie's burial, Bea suggested Brenda stay on since they had been together for so long. Brenda was Bea's last link to Maggie. Maggie and Bea had shared the same home for so long. She didn't want to be alone. Brenda, who had become family, wanted to make sure Bea's life recovered from the sadness of what happened to Maggie.

Brenda joined Bea at the restaurant and gradually encouraged Bea to join the dancing cocoon of friends. Over time, they started dancing. The librarian, who had always avoided other people, joined them—and danced. Brenda cheered her on, just as she had cheered on Maggie's everyday, always encouraging more, always a support.

On that day when Bea was unable to swing her legs from the bed, and experienced a massive stroke, it was Brenda who came to her aide. With extensive physical therapy, Bea gained the use of her right arm and hand—but only her right arm and hand. She knew that she needed to rely solely on Brenda to survive. Thus, Brenda is now caregiver again.

Maggie needed Bea, Bea needed Brenda, and Brenda needed friends—not just clients—whom she could care for and nurture. Maggie had worked so hard, and propelled the small family business into a multi-million dollar powerhouse. In the end, her life's work covered the cost of Brenda staying with her full-time, and then Brenda staying with Bea full-time. Brenda is aware of the great investment the two sisters made in her. She is also grateful for the trust and sense of family and friendship that they provided her.

Under one roof that needed trust and hope, grew the seedlings of fresh respect. Needs are blunted. Like a revolving door: need to need to need.

14 - Doing it Our Way

Felice, Beth and Mary—just five years from the first to the third. Sisters and life-long best friends.

Strangers see them and think they are triplets, because they are all alike in so many ways—the way they all clap their hands when they start laughing, the way they walk with their heads tilted slightly to the side, the soft sound of their voices, and the quick wit they display when caught in awkward situations.

They are always together—always sharing with, supporting, and confiding in each other. They have a bond that friends, boy friends and even husbands will never match. They share the bond of growing up under the roof of an old-country, domineering father, whose most constant order to each of them was: "Do it my way." The three grew up, shrinking from any sense of individual worth as he screamed constantly to "Do it my way."

In the early years, they did it his way. When their father yelled at Felice to stop moving the stool near the sofa, little Mary, just learning to walk, tottered over to the stool, pushing at it, knowing that Felice was a few seconds away from more yelling if the stool wasn't back in the right spot, perfectly placed for their father to rest his feet upon when reading the paper. Little Mary developed a private code with her sisters before she could say more than a few words. Each sister knew when the others needed help, and as they grew older, each knew when the others needed to find a way to "do it her way."

It wasn't a code with symbols, but more of an emotional code, where smiles, frowns, tears, indicated what was needed. The pleading tone in Beth's voice when she asked to stay after school for a special school program told Felice and Mary that they needed to step in quickly, and offer to do Beth's chores before her father had a chance to say "no." They learned how to work together, how to quietly resist their father, and do things their way, even though he thought it was his way. In doing so, they found their way toward independence.

As each left home, they celebrated freedom of choice and achievement, promising never to impose "their way" on their own children. They also celebrated a special bond. To this day, they don't compete with each other. Their relationship isn't mired in sibling rivalry. They aren't jealous of, and they don't judge, each other. They offer constructive criticism when necessary and are each others greatest supporters. They still share everything from clothes and jewelry to a love of Italian cooking and dancing.

Through strains in marriages and career ups and downs—even when they were separated by great distances—their bond was strong. They all left Cape Cod as young adults, but knew they would all return one day.

Though some of their earliest Cape Cod childhood memories are among the darkest memories of their lives, Cape Cod is where

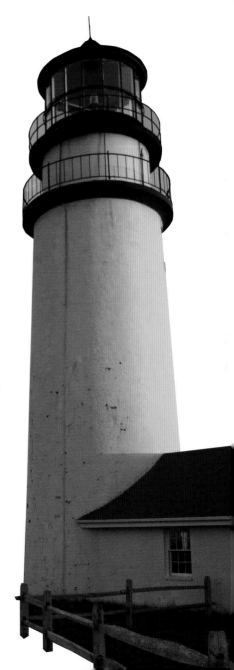

they formed their bond, where they learned at an early age the importance of establishing their own identities, while working together as a team, always supporting each other—always sisters finding their own way.

Where there is reconciliation and strong love, there is peace, harmony, serenity, and stronger twines in the rope of family and pals.

15 - The Race Is On

It was a show-stopping ring. More than five carats of Tiffany & Co. at its very best: platinum setting, with channel-set diamonds all the way around the band, leading to the pièce de résistance—an emerald-cut pink diamond.

"How many people have you seen with a pink diamond?" Becky asked her best friend Marge. Marge smiled and shrugged her shoulders. She'd never even heard of a pink diamond.

Becky's husband, Ed, demonstrated his success by "baubling" Becky to be the optimal vision: a standing-walking-dancing emblem of his own high achievements. Becky dressed in couture fashion, accessorized with expensive jewelry, drove a showy car, and lived in the biggest house, in the very best neighborhood. Becky wanted for naught.

Marge, on the other hand, struggled with the question: "Why not me?" Her few pieces of jewelry were costume jewelry. Her clothes were always bought on sale, from discount stores. Her car was on its last leg, and her home was in need of repair. However, she would not allow her personal comparisons to Becky put strains on their friendship. Instead, she bit down hard on her inner lip whenever the envy genie appeared. Marge learned to accept what is—and let it be. Though she struggled with comparisons from time to time, she was never in a race to compete.

Then one day, Marge saw the "For Sale" sign on Becky's home. Becky laughed off Marge's questions, saying they no longer needed the space. They didn't have kids at home, and they wanted a smaller home, easier to leave and return to when travelling. Then Becky's trendy BMW was replaced with a reliable truck. A truck, really? Marge saw Becky in the grocery story parking lot, pulling away. Marge waved, but Becky didn't wave back.

When Ed decided to sell some of Becky's jewelry, Becky finally broke down and told Marge that they'd overspent, invested poorly, and lost their retirement savings. They had tons of stuff, but what they needed was cash. Becky had all the right clothes and the amazing jewelry, yet she didn't have enough saved to pay her bills.

Ed and Becky's world imploded. Within a few brief months they witnessed a waterfall runoff of all those tangible assets that served as beacon lights of their importance—their success, their lofty perch compared to those around them.

Marge, friend that she was, was the first to comfort Becky, as she learned the severity of their financial losses. Ed and Becky had put so much psychic value on money, only to watch it drain away in front of them.

"Starting over" is an understatement when describing how Ed and Becky had to adjust. Although retired, Ed and Becky had to accept humbling part-time jobs just to sustain their minimal lifestyle. Ed started work for a local t-shirt shop, which specializes in custom-stitching company names on collar shirts. He is back where he started more than 40 year ago, making cold calls, contacting other businesses, except this time the work he's trying to drum up is for the t-shirt shop. Becky took a position at the local grocery story, working the cash register. It is hard for customers to miss the few rings still on her fingers as she rings up their items. Every now and then someone makes a comment and Becky simply smiles in return, never offering a verbal response.

As time passed, they found themselves adjusting to their simple, but pleasing, monk-like lives. All the glitter of high-class jewelry is gone, as is the glitter of their former lives.

Marge had always saved her money. She didn't take big risks with her investments, and was relatively safe when the economic down-turn devastated Becky's life. Through the years, she'd been putting small amounts away here and there, saving for a gift to herself—her own diamond ring. Over an afternoon tea with Becky, she showed her the new ring.

Unlike Marge, who had bitten that lip and disciplined herself to chase the envy genie from her mind, Becky allowed envy to eat through her friendship with Marge. She could not get past comparing her now barren lifestyle to what she interpreted as Marge's success. Becky lacked the wisdom to choose friendship over envy.

However, wisdom had not left Marge. She sensed the growing gap with Becky. She concluded that the diamond ring was the symbol that Becky could not accept. She sold that diamond ring and arranged for another afternoon tea with Becky.

Marge lifted her ringless finger and said: "The race is over. Our friendship is the winner. Diamonds aren't forever. Friends are forever."

Marge, Becky and Ed are back to sitting at the same table when they meet their other dancing pals for dinner and dancing. They all know that starting over is the best thing to do—whether you are losing your savings or your best friends. Just stay out of the racing lanes.

Diamonds aren't forever.

Friends are forever.

"Be not afraid of Greatness."

16 - Goobers or Licorice Sticks?

Andrea liked the sound of the peppermint sticks clinking against the glass jars as she moved them from the back room to the front of the store. The sounds of the candy jars soothed her as she approached customers.

Andrea had always been an outgoing child, but when it was time for her to start school, she started turning inward. Andrea speaks with a slight lisp—just enough to attract school-age teasing. Grace, Andrea's mother, worked with Andrea, trying to help her overcome her speech impediment, and conquer her debilitating shyness.

Numbers were Andrea's forte. Grace had always been impressed with Andrea's crisp intelligence—her easy facility with numbers. She took great pride in seeing Andrea attend college and become an actuary for an insurance company.

Sadly, she then had to see Andrea's long struggle with deep shyness render her unable to continue her work. Andrea was simply too shy to handle day-to-day dealings with other people.

When Andrea left her job, Grace decided she would find a place where Andrea could work, which would require socializing with others, but at a slow, gradual pace. Grace repeatedly told her that she would one day find a place where Andrea could learn to mingle with people again—even 'socialize' as she pushed her shyness into a more manageable place in her mind.

When Grace saw the small "Help Wanted" sign in the neighborhood candy store window, she stepped inside to speak with the store's owner. He told her it was difficult to find dependable employees. Most who sought work with him were high school students, whose many interests impeded their reliability. His dream, he said, was to find someone who could be his dependable back-of-store organizer—someone who knew how the store experience improved for customers as the bins were filled with wide varieties of candy.

Grace told him about Andrea. She explained that she was a bit slow in her movements because she was shy, and that she found speaking to others a challenge. Grace then underscored Andrea's aptitude for numbers, and the fact that she is reliable. He agreed to interview Andrea for the job.

When Grace told Andrea about the candy store job, Andrea whined, claiming it would be impossible for her to be around strangers—to speak to strangers.

Grace persisted, and encouraged Andrea to make the effort since she would be secure in the back room, and not have to deal with strangers. Andrea gave in and went with her mother to meet the store owner.

When they met, the owner explained the job requirements to Andrea. She would be in the back room, organizing, and thinking about displays for the front of the store. She would not have to deal with the customers. Though he knew it would be a while before Andrea was comfortable enough to even talk to him on his own, the owner could tell that she was reliable, steady, and trustworthy. He offered her the job, she accepted, and he handed her a royal blue smock with the candy store logo embroidered on it. The smock was Andrea's first uniform. It offered her a sense of belonging.

Andrea thrived in the new job. She took great pride in making sure the customers enjoyed being in the store. She loved hearing the ohhs and ahhs as people spotted candy they hadn't eaten since childhood. She lived through the laughter and memories shared in the store.

Within a few months of starting the job, the owner told Andrea he would offer her a salary increase. He also wanted to offer her more responsibility—working with customers at the candy counter. Andrea was both thrilled at the recognition and terrified at the idea of having to speak to customers. She was just too shy, she thought.

The owner explained that he would work side by side with her until she felt ready to step out on her own. Comforted by the team idea, Andrea agreed to give the new position a shot.

After a week of teaming with the owner, Andrea discovered that if she asked a question of a customer, the customer would smile, and that smile tended to reduce her own shyness.

She experimented with several questions, until she found the question that prompted the most smiles: "Goobers or licorice sticks?"

In time Andrea became at home as both the back-store organizer and the customer service person. Repeat customers often arrive at the store, and upon seeing Andrea, try to beat her to the punch, asking her: "Goobers or licorice sticks?" They are warmed by the familiarity of the question. It is Andrea's trademark link to so many customers.

The candy store is a few blocks away from the cocoon dancers' favored club. Often, when walking home from her evening shifts at the store, Andrea stopped and listened to the music floating to the street. While standing there one evening, a candy store customer saw her and invited her to come in and listen to the music as his guest.

Although frightened by the idea of being with so many strangers, Andrea was comforted by his accompanying her and, for the first time ever, went into a place filled with happy dancers.

Within minutes, a parade of people came to greet her—welcome her—each one saying with a smile: "Goobers or licorice sticks?" With that warm and welcome embrace, Andrea found comfort. She started going to the club twice a week, following her evening shifts at the store.

After many visits, she actually agreed to dance with one of the candy store regulars.

As weeks went by, Andrea found that she could dance, could chat amiably, and could join with the others to enjoy the music and the company. The club became her third home—after her house and the candy store. However she never stayed late since she knew her mother, Grace, was awake and waiting for her safe arrival home.

Since she never wanted to simply leave the club, she decided to end every dance evening by walking to her various dance partners and say: "Thank you for a nice evening. I just want to say good night."

Andrea ended every club evening with that new ritual. And a ritual developed within that ritual: When Andrea got to each dance partner to say good night, each would wave to her and say "Goobers or licorice sticks?"

Andrea is now in the cocoon as a welcome pal. Her life has a sense of extended family, of joy, of abundant kindness.

17 - Rafael's Cupcake

"It's my birthday," Rafael mumbled, as his cocoon friends joined him at the bar. Their congratulations and good wishes were met with, "Having an awful time. Am old—cracking the big 75."

Except for the cocoon friends embracing him, it was clear Rafael was spending his 75th birthday alone.

He stares at his face in the mirror every morning, examining the deeper lines around his eyes, his forehead, and his mouth. The once-cut jaw has a softer edge to it. His hair is still full, but now gray. It is a daily struggle for him to look back at the face staring at him in the mirror. The face of today reminds him of all the might-have-beens of yesterday.

Rafael is the youngest of three brothers—a good 10 years younger than the older two. As a child, he enjoyed the attention his brothers' girlfriends gave him. He was a cute kid—and charming. He just had to smile, and he was immediately welcomed wherever he went. As he grew into high school, he was the big man on campus. Though he didn't excel in sports or academics, he excelled in good looks. A party wasn't a party unless Rafael was there. Every girl wanted to be seen holding his hand, and every guy wanted to be Rafael.

Everything came easily to him. The teachers gave him breaks because he was so charming, and in his after-school job at a car dealership, he merely had to show that smile, and once-potential customers became "definites" following closely as he led them to the sales rep to close the deal.

After high school, he started working full time. However, things weren't as easy. He was older. People expected him to work. Rafael started bouncing—from one job to the next, flashing that smile, charming managers during his interviews. He was an ace interviewee. He knew what people wanted to hear. And, of course, handsome. He wasn't afraid to leave a job if things got hard because it was always easy to find a new job. Though Rafael did take a cue and started working in earnest, Rafael's loyalty was to Rafael.

Rafael's personal relationships were on and off, mirroring his work. When things got difficult, he moved on, knowing that he could easily find new pals and girlfriends. He'd always been able to do that in the past.

Now, as he looks in the mirror, he also sees the reflection of so many loves and friends lost. He did marry, but it was a one-sided marriage. Both individuals focused on Rafael. No children. And, his wife died from cancer at a young age.

On Cape Cod, a childhood friend, one of the few still in Rafael's life, introduced him to the cocoon pals. There were a number of single dancers. Rafael thought he would meet someone, maybe find a new girlfriend.

Despite his efforts, none of the single women in the group were interested in anything other than friendship. They'd all met others like Rafael in the past—a lot of fun, but not there for the long haul. They were there for dancing, and perhaps friendship, nothing more.

Rafael did something he'd never done in the past: he stuck with the group of friends. When a friend needed help fixing something in her home, Rafael was the go-to guy. In the past, he had focused on his own needs, and within the cocoon of friends, found himself focusing on their needs.

The friends introduced Rafael to a different kind of beauty—one that comes from within. They taught him to see the beauty in deeds and not in looks.

Rafael's grouchiness at turning 75 years old was an acknowledgment of knowing—with trumpet clarity—that his tomorrows would be too brief to completely change the results of 75 years of self-focus. Save for the new cocoon friends, he was alone—completely without anyone in his life.

Despite his grouchy demeanor on the night of his birthday, he smiled when the bartender walked from the kitchen toward him. A small plate held in his two hands embraced a single cupcake, with a single lit flickering candle upon it. The flame threatened to fade as the bartender walked toward Rafael, but the bartender was patient. He stopped to wait for the flame to regain intensity—similar to the cocoon friends who waited for Rafael to gain an intensity that shone for others, and made others happy and smile.

Had he not met these cocoon pals, he would have been alone that night. Instead, as they sang "Happy Birthday" to him, he smiled, tears running down his face, a sign of happiness, rather than sadness.

As the birthday wishers finished singing, the bartender came out with a full birthday cake. Rafael walked from table to table, delivering bantam slices of cake to each friend.

His tears were also tears of gratitude for the embrace and non-judgment by his cocoon dancing pals.

They did not take note of Rafael's yesterdays. They only knew him as a deeply caring, highly competent "Mr. Fixit" who delighted in being useful–always on call–to his Cape Cod friends. Each of them knew that–whatever the problem–the first call they should make was to Rafael.

And they took comfort in knowing he would be their first responder. Always.

18 - One O'clock
Walk to the Mail Box

Julia's laughter is as constant as breathing. Always laughing–infectious and inviting. Her laughter transforms her from a petite stranger to the larger than life, most important person in the room.

The night I met her at the Yacht club, she reminded me of actress Jessica Tandy, petite, always poised and sophisticated–neat and finished in her white pant suit and matching shell necklace and earrings. She sat quietly listening to another Yacht club member's story about the rigor of his daily workout routine.

He described every machine used, every exercise embraced, and every Pilates move endured. He emphasized how much time he spent at the gym every day, and talked about the importance of wearing good, not just expensive sneakers, and discussed the pros and cons of different energy drinks and diets.

Julia listened, intently and respectfully. However, her laugh was rumbling up from deep inside her as she looked at the "workout guy"— his tummy tipped over the table lid, and his shirt was bursting at the seams. He was a clear fifty pounds overweight. The food and drinks in front of him flew in the face of everything he'd been talking about. Though he talked diet, the food he ate in rhythm to his constant talking didn't appear within any of the advocated four major food groups.

Julia was impelled to change the subject lest she laugh out loud at the contrast between the exercises described and the reality of the describer's girth.

Julia smiled and said "my principle daily workout is my 1 o'clock walk to the mailbox!" That was just enough of a subject change to allow her a smile, and suppress her laugh.

Julia is an accomplished, caring woman, who guided her children to be the same way. Though her physical activities involve more than a quick 1 o'clock walk to the mailbox, she did not share that with the gentleman. She did not like talking about herself. She preferred listening to others—except when the others are so self-focused as to be wearisome.

Later that evening, I asked her about her friends and family, and was pleased when she opened up to me. When asked about her male pals, Julia joked that her earlier marriages coaxed her into comfort in only having men as pals—cocoon dancers who only wanted/needed to be "friends."

Smiling from her polished wooden window seat, Julia observed:

"I have found love comes in different stages and intensity: once vital married love can fade to be only endurance love. Puppy love too often becomes hard to chew. Sensual love settles into routine love. The love of true friends is an always blessing garden of new flowers. Being with loving friends is a great pond of peace. The privilege of being among true friends is so satisfying."

She smiled softly in reflection of what she had just said. She looked at her table mates and added:

"To be sure—if any of my friends needed me at any time, I would do my best to be there for them."

Musing thoughtfully and looking at the friend who had offered the detailed description of his daily workout routine, Julia added in kindness: "For my friends there cannot be a time or distance barrier—they matter in my life. It is my thoughts about my cocoon pals that make my 1 o'clock walk to the mailbox so pleasing."

Courage, Kindness & Truth

"I am as constant as the Northern Star."

19 - The Magnetic Personality

Dianne is always ready with a "warm welcome"—whether joining friends at the yacht club, the restaurant, or the dance club. She always has time—always with a bright smile, kind words, and a genuine interest in catching up with the cocoon of Cape Cod friends.

Her warmth invites equal warmth.

Indeed, wherever she is, whomever she is with, she draws people to her—like a magnet. Dianne is easy to talk to and she is the first one called when counsel is needed. Her listening and guiding skills are admired as much as they are respected.

Everyone wants to be with her. Simply standing next to Dianne invites a good feeling about one's self. Her kind comments and caring ways are complimented by her external beauty, too. Her colorful outfits and matching jewelry make everyone smile.

Natural and beauty are two words that come to mind when Dianne is in the room. She is never overdressed. Never outspoken. She is even. Balanced.

Her flowing skirts swirl as she dances with cocoon pals. Her wavy blonde hair bounces to the beat of the music—a regular Ginger Rogers. Eyes are drawn to her as she dances across the floor. Even without speaking, that magnetic personality is evident.

Upon gentle probing I learned that Dianne has both an undergraduate and master's degree in counseling. Her professional life embraced a series of leadership roles—all linked by the focus of serving others with those same gifts of listening, hearing, guiding, and counseling that her cocoon pals value today. Her magnetic personality was strengthened in her professional world before entering the life chapter of welcome retirement

Because Dianne is naturally good humored, so quick with a smile and laugh, so abundant in sharing of herself, it is easy to conclude her life path has always been clear, smooth, and progressing.

However, "clear" was modified by two marriages that covered more than thirty years of her life—one fogged by alcohol and the other by deceit.

Dianne's "smooth" resembled a choppy ocean as she set out to gain an education, while working sixty hour weeks, plus college classes, plus being a single mother of three daughters.

"Progressing" had been marred by unplanned financial reversals—an occasional supervisor who resented Dianne's persistent ambition to BE college educated.

During those several years, sleep—consistent, normal sleep—was not to be. There were many weeks when, over a three day period, Dianne's sleep would be measured in brief minutes—not hours. She disciplined herself to function in work and college and as a mother, while in a state of perpetual fatigue.

She also had to discipline herself to her harsh economic reality. Even with volunteering to work the equivalent of another half week to gain the overtime pay, her income was limited and her resources scarce. In four years of college she only used text books from the library. She could not afford to buy a single book. Yet, she absorbed the learning, gained the information, and conquered the course work.

During those several years of sacrifice, time after time, Dianne would bite down on the steel plate of her tough reality. She, metaphorically, infused her teethmarks into that bar of steel put in her life path as a challenge. She did not yield to the tough steel. She could not break it, but she did prevent it from breaking her.

She bargain shopped for her daughters, and made her own necklaces and bracelets to give them for their birthdays.

She learned to live life for the day.

She learned how to find joy in a day-tight compartment.

She learned to carry the weight of her challenges, never putting them on others.

She endured and grew.

She treated others how she wanted to be treated, and in doing so, drew others toward her.

Those early threads of pathos, suffering, and pain were diminished by the cocoon world of her deep friendships, and faded to be occasional, faint memories.

Dianne is who she is—a magnetic personality, attracting others to access her abundance—all because she long ago confronted reality as being "it is what it is."

Dianne chose to do whatever it took to create the always new, always growing, always giving Dianne.

Loneliness is a choice. Abundant living is also a choice. Should you be one of those gripped in low-level sadness—with no sense of greater purpose to your life—determine this minute to reach up, reach out and find new joy with new faces, new friends, new purpose.

And as one embraces common interests with others—functioning in your own shared activities—seek opportunities to build a cocoon of caring, of support, of "being there" for each other.

Those opportunities are the building blocks in creating those 'cocoons of comfort.'

Work to understand the reality of the spectrum of human conditions, issues, life journeys represented in each individual member of your cocoon.

Shakespeare's works endure because he captured basic truths of the human condition.

Every member of your shared activity deserves the respect and understanding for their own life issues. When in your cocoon of comfort—those life issues are made more manageable—less threatening.

It is when you can nurture a shared activity to become a caring, nurturing, supportive element that the notion of a cocoon can embrace your life.

"It is not in the stars
to hold our destiny
but in ourselves."

20 - Butterfly Splendor

The individual stories of each cocoon pal have strengthened the exterior shell of the cocoon. The pattern rendered is vibrant and engaging, a peek at what the cocoon holds within.

Inside the cocoon, the pals have grown and developed. They've conquered hardships together, and embraced happiness together. Though each is different—each still an individual—together they are one. Seeing them together as a group, they are a beautiful butterfly.

In these years of their retirement, they've come together, evolving into a beautiful butterfly. They once walked, now they fly (and dance). Their wings spread slowly, opening to an expansive spread of beauty that mirrors their experiences, emotions, and personalities. They've nurtured the inner beauty of the cocoon, and in doing so, grew into a butterfly of mythical beauty and proportions.

Shakespeare's core themes live in the lives of the Cape Cod cocoon pals. Yet when they are together, they transcend. They've lived Shakespeare, but they learned and now exist as a beautiful butterfly.

Reflections

As noted at the beginning in Invitations, we want to repeat the noble purpose of the book. There may be only a few who have thumbed these pages, whose lives are dulled with loneliness—with quiet desperation to find joy, meaning, illumination, even simple fresh friendships.

And for those few this message of the cocoon dancing pals may be just the candle of new light you are seeking to fill voids and purpose in your life.

The message is to move out, move on, move forward to put yourself into situations that engage you and other people. These need not be deep or complex programs, but they do require you to take that action step and embrace common interests with other people.

Look for local library reading groups, look for adult school study programs, look for area dance lesson groups, look for any interesting program that merely requires you to seek it out and join it.